Favourite Melodies for Flute
Easy to play arrangements by
David Sumbler

We hope you enjoy *Favourite Melodies for Flute*.
Further copies are available from your local music shop.

In case of difficulty, please contact the publisher direct:

The Sales Department
KEVIN MAYHEW LTD
Rattlesden
Bury St Edmunds
Suffolk IP30 0SZ

Phone 01449 737978
Fax 01449 737834

Please ask for our complete catalogue of Instrumental Music.

Front Cover: *The Love Letter* by Henry John King (1855-1924).
Reproduced by kind permission of Graham Gallery, London/
Fine Art Photographic Library, London.

Cover designed by Juliette Clarke and Graham Johnstone.
Picture Research: Jane Rayson.

First published in Great Britain in 1995 by Kevin Mayhew Ltd

© Copyright 1995 Kevin Mayhew Ltd

ISBN 0 86209 612 X
Catalogue No: 3611141

All or part of these pieces have been arranged by
David Sumbler and are the copyright of Kevin Mayhew Ltd.

Music Editor: Anthea Smith
Music Setting: Louise Hill

Printed and bound in Great Britain

Contents

DAVID SUMBLER (b. 1947), who arranged the music in this book, is Principal Flautist with the Northern Ballet Theatre Orchestra. He has also played with many of the major orchestras including the BBC Philharmonic, Hallé and the City of Birmingham Symphony Orchestra.

David Sumbler works as a composer, arranger, pianist and adjudicator, and is also an examiner for the Trinity College of Music, London.

GYMNOPÉDIE II

Erik Satie (1866 - 1925)

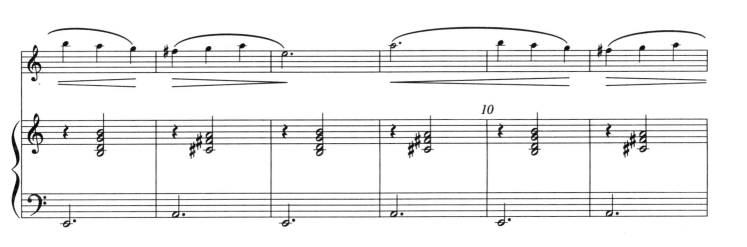

6

7

THE MERMAID

Traditional English Melody

BALLATA from RIGOLETTO

Giuseppe Verdi (1813 - 1901)

TIT-WILLOW from THE MIKADO

Arthur Sullivan (1842 - 1900)

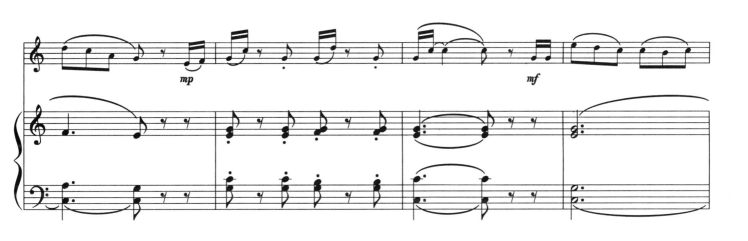

DANCE OF THE SUGAR-PLUM FAIRY

Peter Ilych Tchaikovsky (1840 - 1893)

TO MUSIC

Franz Schubert (1797 - 1828)

ARIETTA

Edvard Grieg (1843 - 1907)

LARGO from NEW WORLD SYMPHONY

Antonín Dvořák (1841 - 1904)

THE KISS

Luigi Arditi (1822 - 1903)

SEBBEN, CRUDELE

Antonio Caldara (c.1670 - 1736)

SANCHO PANZA from DON QUIXOTE

Léon Minkus (1826 - 1917)

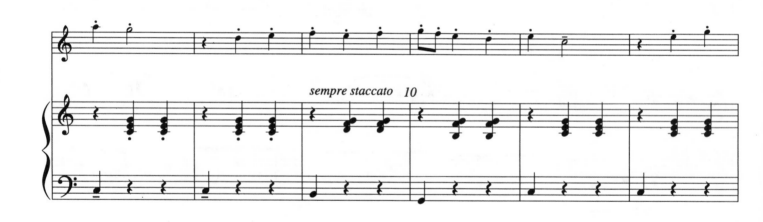

27

PILGRIMS' MARCH from SYMPHONY No. 4

Felix Mendelssohn (1809 - 1847)

AVE MARIA

J S Bach/Charles Gounod (1818 - 1893)

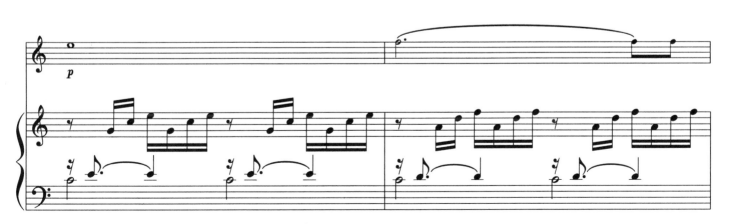

BUGEILIO'R GWENITH GWYN

Traditional Welsh Melody

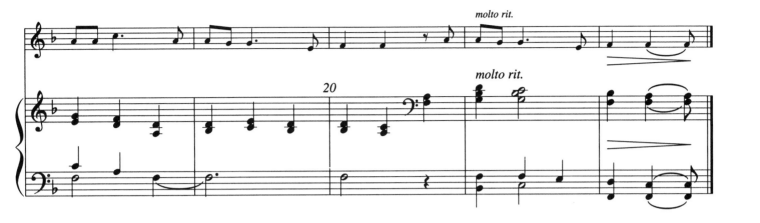

THE QUEENES ALMAN

William Byrd (1543 - 1623)

THEME from PIANO CONCERTO K467

Wolfgang Amadeus Mozart (1756 - 1791)

41

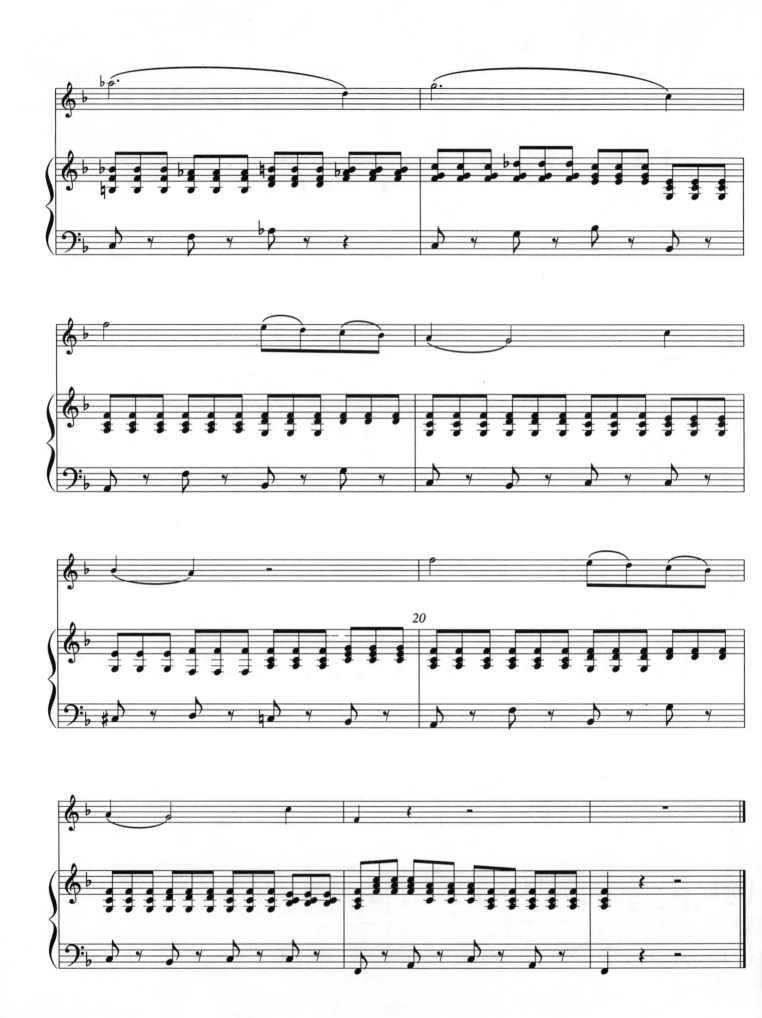

PAVANE POUR UNE INFANTE DÉFUNTE

Maurice Ravel (1875 - 1937)

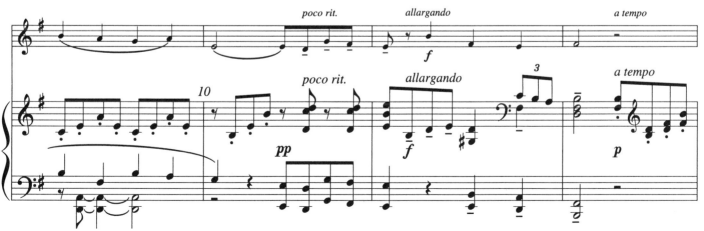

ROMANZA

Anon.

47

1 GREEN

1 Part Barrel.

(Set/12)